It's Easy To Play Pops 6.

Wise Publications
London/New York/Paris/Sydney/Copenhagen/Madrid

Exclusive Distributors:
Music Sales Limited
8/9 Frith Street, London W1V 5TZ, England.
Music Sales Pty Limited
120 Rothschild Avenue, Rosebery, NSW 2018, Australia.

Order No.AM91212
ISBN 0-7119-3456-8

Art direction by Michael Bell Design.
Cover illustration by Frank Langford
Compiled by Peter Evans
Music arranged by Frank Booth
Music processed by Ternary Graphics

Printed in the United Kingdom by
Caligraving Limited, Thetford, Norfolk.

Achy Breaky Heart

Words & Music by Don Von Tress

D
floor, or you can tell my lips to tell my fin - ger - tips they
won't be reach-ing out for you no more. (But)
Chorus
G
G
don't tell my heart, my
a - chy break-y heart, I just don't think he'd un - der - stand. And
D
if you tell my heart, my a - chy break - y heart, he
might blow up and kill this man.
G
(Instrumental)
G

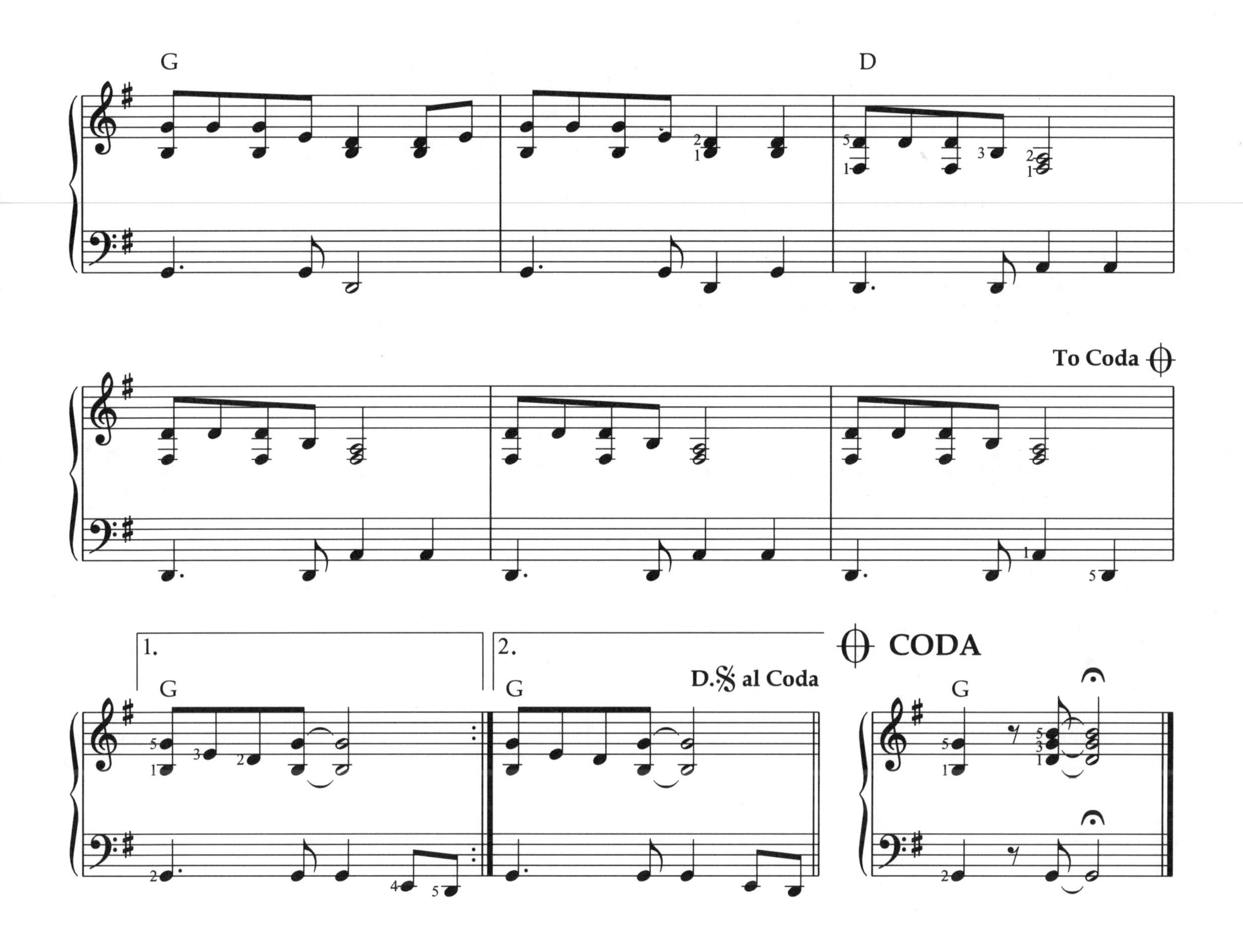

Verse 2

You can tell your ma I moved to Arkansas,
You can tell your dog to bite my leg.
Or tell your brother Cliff whose fist can tell my lip
That he never really liked me anyway.
Or tell your Aunt Louise, tell anything you please,
Myself already knows I'm not okay,
Or you can tell my eyes to watch out for my mind,
It might be walking out on me today.

(Everything I Do) I Do It For You

Moderately

Words by Bryan Adams & Robert John 'Mutt' Lange
Music by Michael Kamen

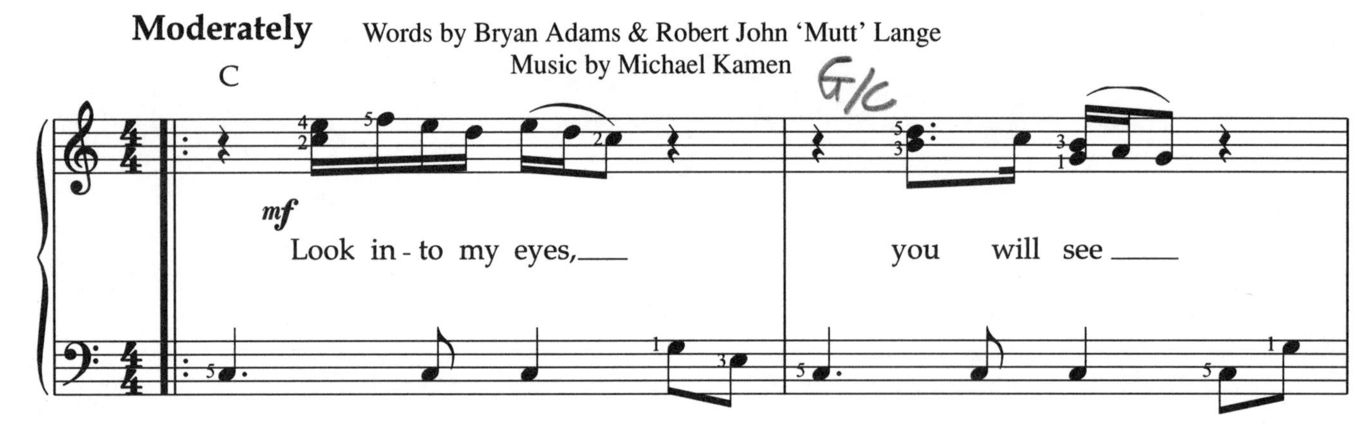

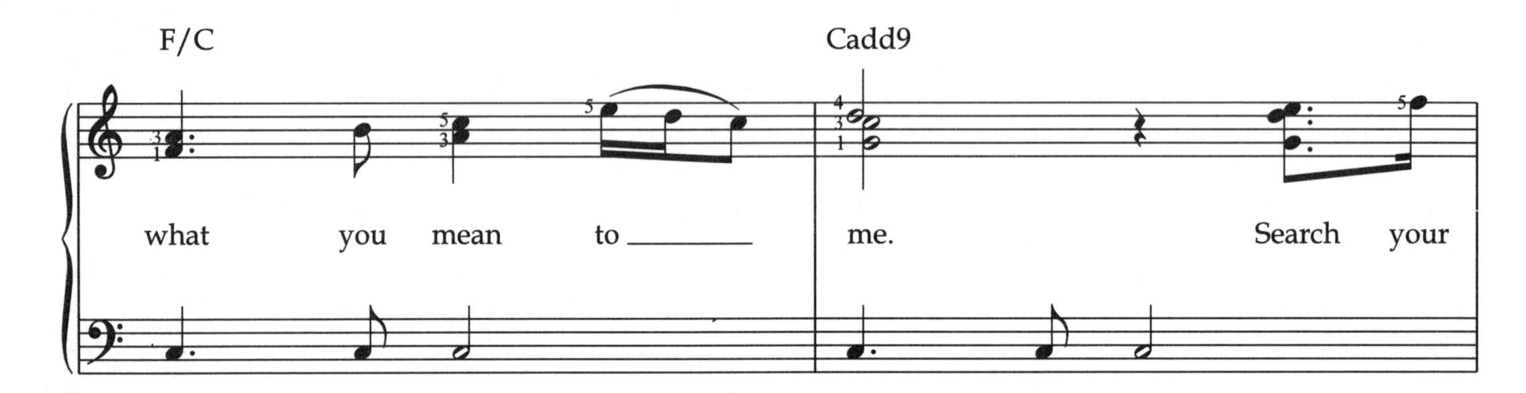

Dm
C
Dm
for, you can't tell me it's not worth dy - in' for. You know it's
C
G
true ev - 'ry - thing I do, I do it for
C
1.
2.
you. There's
B♭
E♭
B♭
no love like your love and no oth - er could give
F
C
G
more love, there's no - where un - less you're there all the

D
G
time, all the way yeah.
F
C
1.
2.
Dm
Oh you can't tell me it's not worth try - in'
G
Dm
for, I can't help it, there's noth - in' I want
G
C
G
more. Yeah I would fight for you, I'd lie for you, walk the

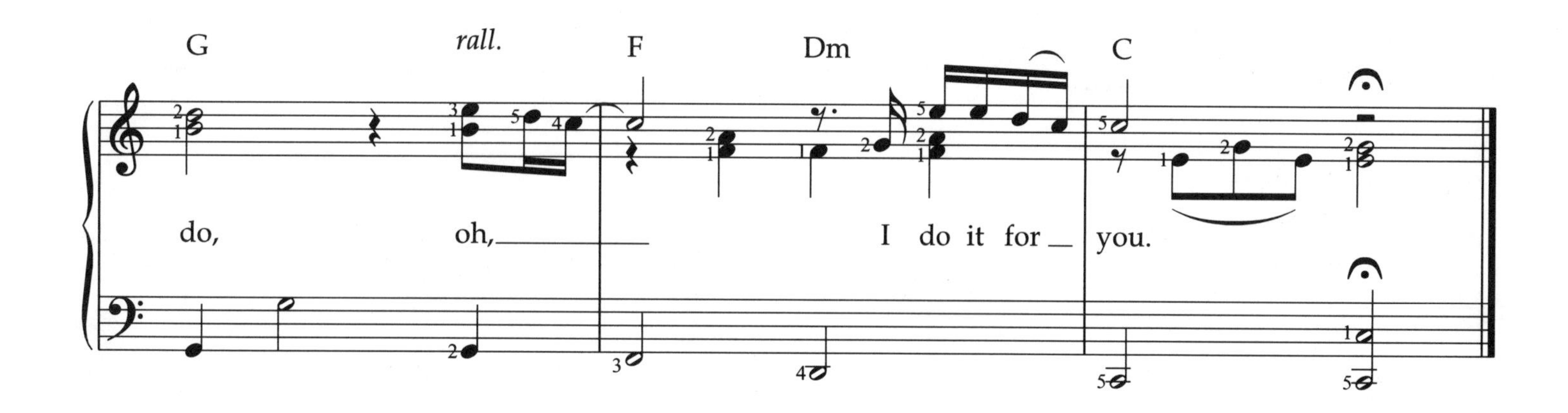

Verse 2

Look into your heart,
You will find there's nothin' there to hide.
Take me as I am, take my life,
I would give it all, I would sacrifice.

Don't tell me it's not worth fightin' for,
I can't help it, there's nothin' I want more.
You know it's true, everything I do,
I do it for you.

From A Distance

Words & Music by Julie Gold

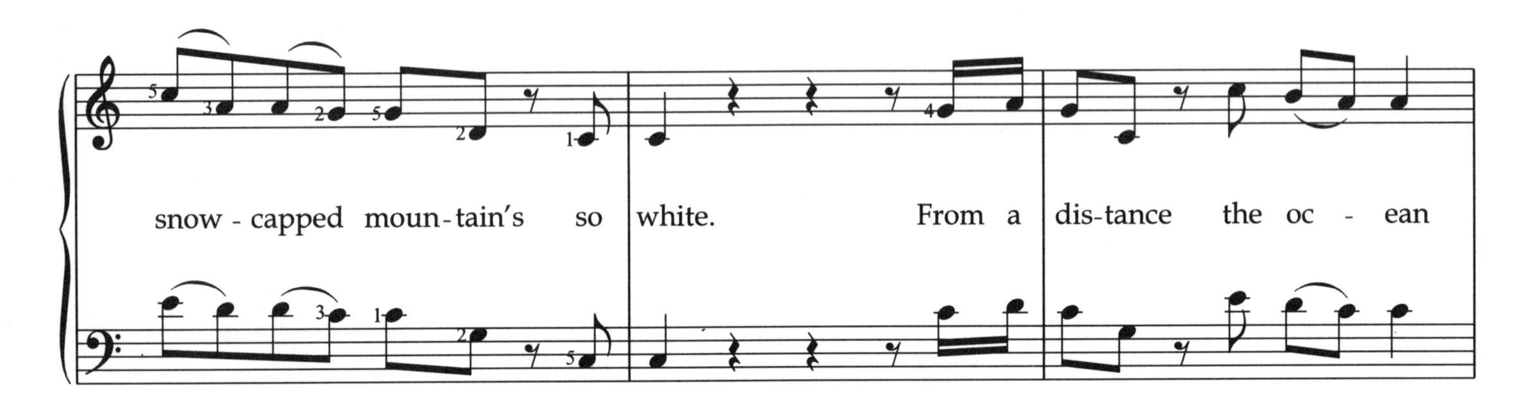

G F C F
It's the voice of hope, it's the voice of peace, its the
F Gsus4 G C G/C bass F/C G/C C G/C F/C
voice 'ev - 'ry - one.
mf
From a
C F G C F Gsus4 G
dis-tance we all have e-nough, and no one is in
C G F G C F G Am G
need. There are no guns, no bombs and no dis-ease, no
F G C G C F G
hun - gry mouths to feed. For a mo-ment we must be

Am
F
C/E
Gsus4
G
in - stru - ments march - ing in a com - mon band. Playing
mp
F
C
F
C
F
Gsus4
G
songs of hope, play - ing songs of peace, they're the songs of ev - 'ry
C
C
F
G
one. God is watch - ing us, God is
C
G/B
Am
F
Gsus4
G
C
F
G
watch - ing us, God is watch - ing us from a dis - tance.
C
G/C
F/C
G
C
N.C.
f
mp
From a dis - tance you look

like my friend, even though we are at war.
From a
mf
C F Gsus4 G Am G F Gsus4 G
dis-tance I can't com - - pre-hend what all this war is
C G C F G Am
for. What we need is love and har-mo-ny, let it
F C/E Gsus4 G F C
e-cho through the land. It's the hope of hopes, it's the
mp
F C F Gsus4 G Am
love of loves, it's the heart of ev - 'ry - one. It's the
cresc.

F C F F Gsus4 G
hope of hopes, it's the love of loves, it's the song of ev - 'ry -
C G/C F/C G/C C G/C F/C C Eaug
f
- one. Sing out songs of hope, sing out
F Gsus4 G C Eaug
songs of free - dom, sing out songs of love, sing out
F Gsus4 G Eaug
songs of peace, sing out songs of jus - tice, sing out
Repeat and fade
F Gsus4 G C Eaug F Em Dm G
songs of har-mo-ny, sing out songs of love, sing out ev - 'ry - one. Sing out

Goodnight Girl

Words & Music by Clarke, Cunningham, Mitchell & Pellow

Am7
Am7/D bass
a - bout my good - night girl.
G
Caught up in your wish-ing well, your hopes in - side it,
Em7
take your love and pro - mis - es and make them last,
1.
Am7
you
Am7/D
make them last.
(2.) You
2.
Am7
you
Am7/D
make them last.
G
Caught up in your wish-ing well, your hopes in - side it,
Em7
take your love and pro - mis-

To Coda
Am7
Am7/D
- es and make them last, you make them last.
Cmaj7
Gmaj7
Cmaj7
Does-n't mat-ter how sad I made you, does-n't mat-ter how hard
Gmaj7
Cmaj7
Gmaj7
I've tried. Just re-mem-ber the same old reas - on re -
B♭maj7
D.𝄋 al Coda
- flec - ted in your eyes, you said you wan - ted me.
CODA
C♭maj7
Amaj7
Dmaj9
D♭maj9
C♭maj7
Amaj7
Dmaj9
Fmaj13

I Will Always Love You

Words & Music by Dolly Parton

C F C G7 C G7 C
you. Bit - ter sweet mem - o - ries, that's all
Am C/G F G7 C G7
I am tak - ing with me; good - bye, please don't
C Am C/G F G7
cry, we both know that I'm not what you need, but
C Am F G7 C Am
I will al - ways love you; I will
F G7 C F C
al - - ways love you.

I Wonder Why

Words & Music by Curtis Stigers & Glen Ballard

F/A
B♭
F/G
Chorus
way ___ and you al - ways con - vince me ___ to stay, and I
G F/G G
𝄋 Dm7
Fmaj7
G/A
won - der why we hold on with tears in our eyes and I
F/G G/F
Dm7
F
G/A
won - der why we have to break down to make things all right. And I
G F/G G/F
Dm7
Fmaj7
Gsus4
won - der why I can't seem to tell you good - bye, ___
G
Gsus4
1. G
2. G
___ yeah, I won - der why.

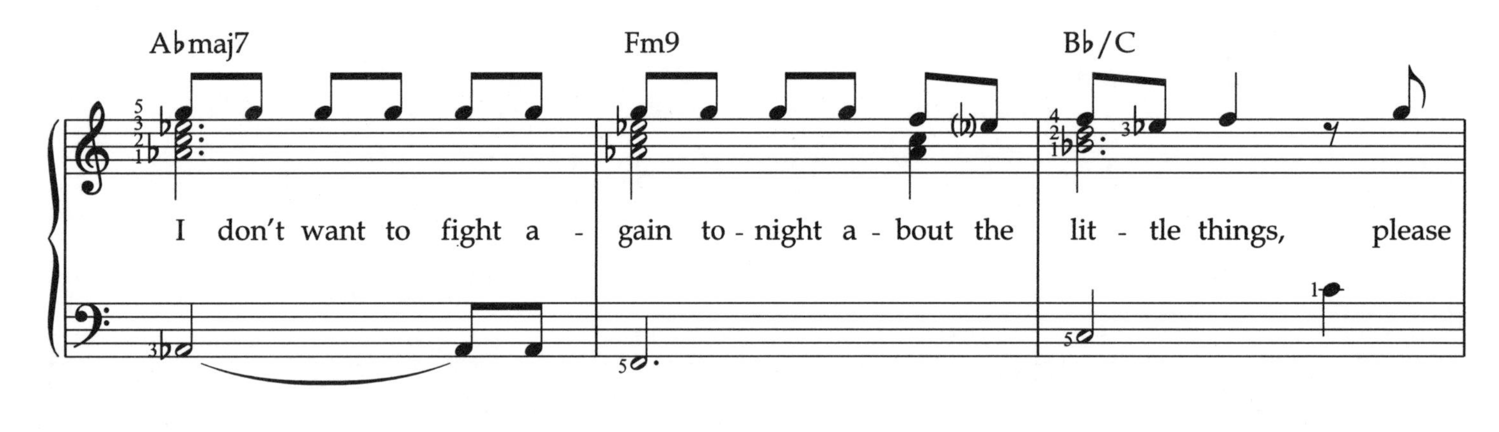

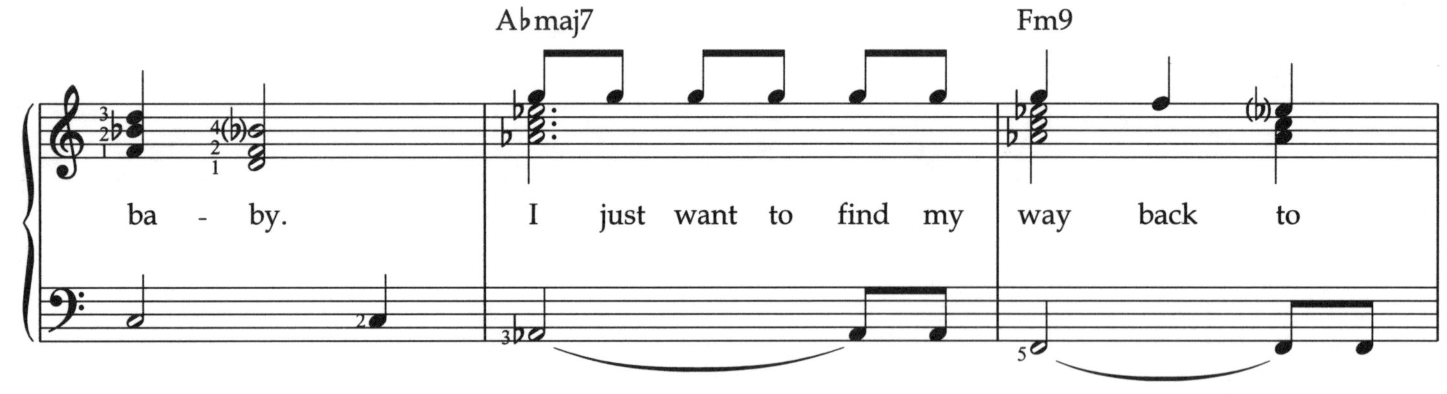

Verse 2

Though I'm no angel
With my selfish pride,
But I love you more
Every day.
Love is an anger
That builds up inside,
As the tears of frustration
Roll down my face.
Why does love always have to turn out
This way?

Chorus 2

And I wonder why we hold on
With tears in our eyes;
And I wonder why we have to break down
To just make things right:
And I wonder why I can't seem
To tell you goodbye,
Oh, I wonder why.

I'm Every Woman

Words & Music by Nickolas Ashford & Valerie Simpson

A tempo, faster
Gm9
C
Gm9
C
Gm9
C
Gm9
C
Gm9
C
Gm9
C
Gm9
C
Gm9
Gm9
Dm7
Gm9
Dm7

Gm9
I'm ev - 'ry wo - man, it's all in me.
omit 2°
C
Dm7
Daug
Gm9
I'm ev - 'ry wo - man, it's all in
me.
C
Dm7
Am7
Gm7
C
Dm7
Am7
Woh woh woh.
Woh woh

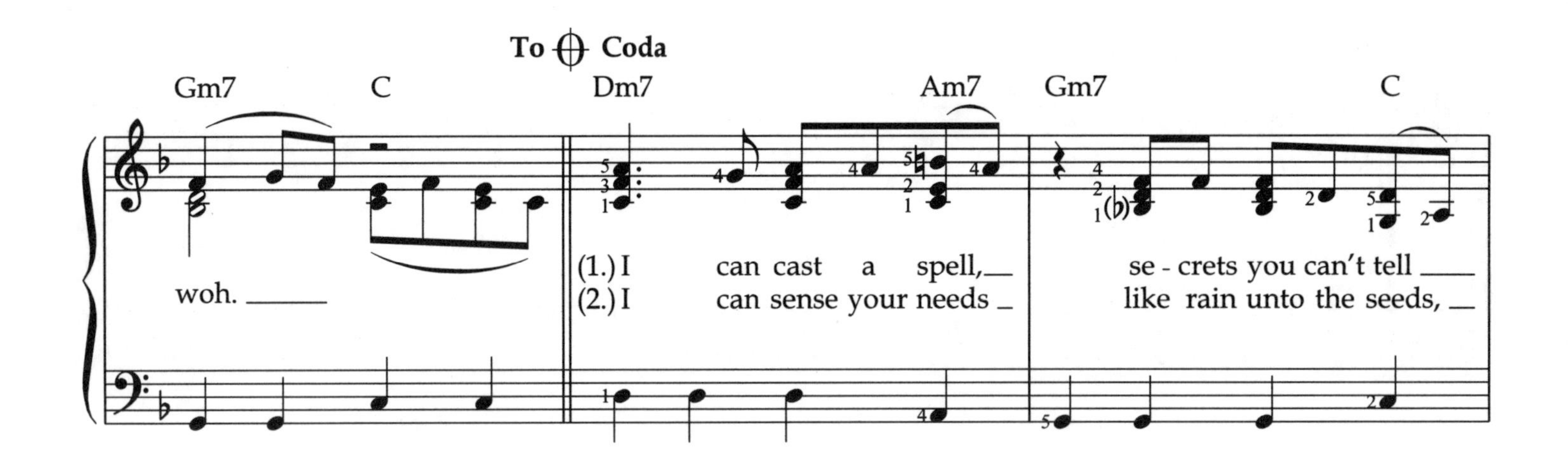
To Coda
Gm7
C
Dm7
Am7
Gm7
C
woh.
(1.) I can cast a spell, se - crets you can't tell
(2.) I can sense your needs like rain unto the seeds,

Dm7
Am7
Gm7
C
Dm7
Am7
makes a spe-cial groove, put fire in-side of you. A - ny - time you fear dan-
I can make a rhyme of confu-sion in your mind. And when it comes down to some

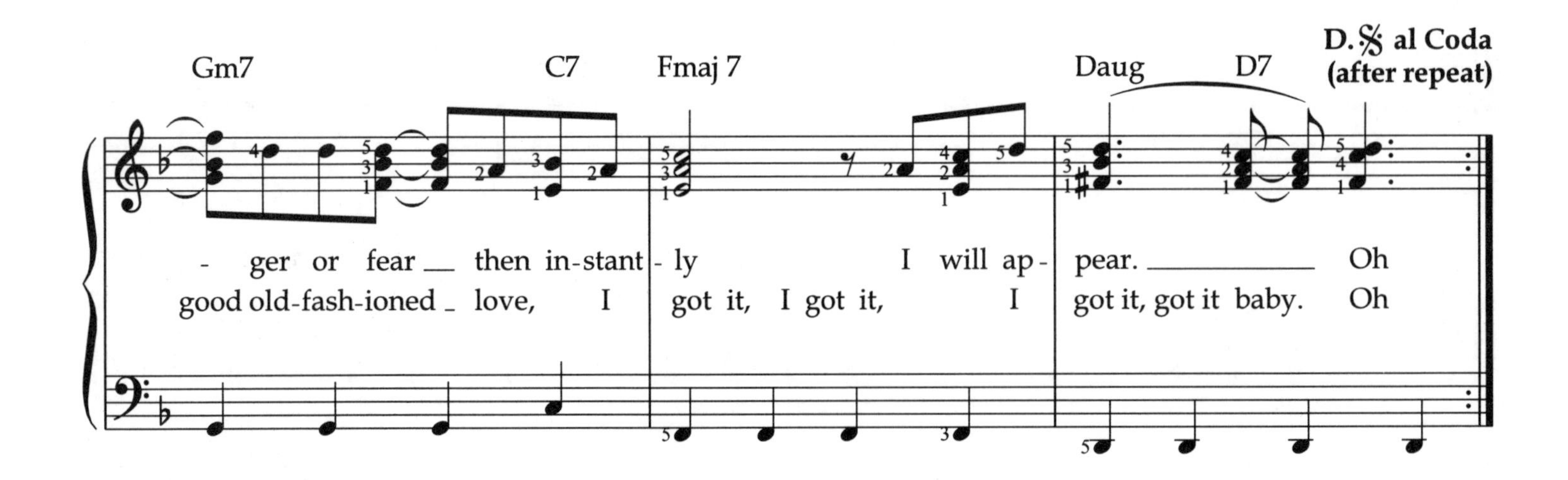
Gm7
C7
Fmaj 7
Daug
D7
D.S. al Coda
(after repeat)
- ger or fear then in-stant - ly I will ap - pear. Oh
good old-fash-ioned love, I got it, I got it, I got it, got it baby. Oh

CODA

Dm7
C
Dm7
C
Dm7
C
I ain't ly - ing, girl, 'cause I'm the one, just act real,

Dm7
C
Dm7
Gm
it shall be done. Don't bo - ther to com-
Dm
Dm7
Am7
Gm7
C
- pare, I've got it.
Woh woh woh.
Fmaj7
E♭m/D
Gm9
C/G
I'm ev - 'ry wo - man,
Gm7
A♭m7 Am7
B♭m7
I'm ev - 'ry wo - man,
I'm ev - 'ry wo -
E♭/B♭
B♭m7
repeat to fade
Am7 A♭m7
- man,
I'm ev - 'ry wo - man.

More Than Words

Words & Music by Nuno Bettencourt & Gary Cherone

G D/F♯ Em Bm7 Am
me how you feel more than words is
D7 G7 C
all you have to do. To make it real, then you would-
Cm G
n't have to say that you love
Em7 Am7 D7
me, 'cause I'd al - rea - - dy
G D/F♯ Em
know. What would you do if my heart

Bm7
C
G/B
Am7
was torn in two, more than words to show you feel
D
G
that your love for me is real. What
D/F♯
Em
Bm7
would you say if I took those words a - way,
To Coda
C
G/B
Am7
D
then you could - n't make things new just by say
G
G/B
Cadd9
Am7
- - ing 'I love you',

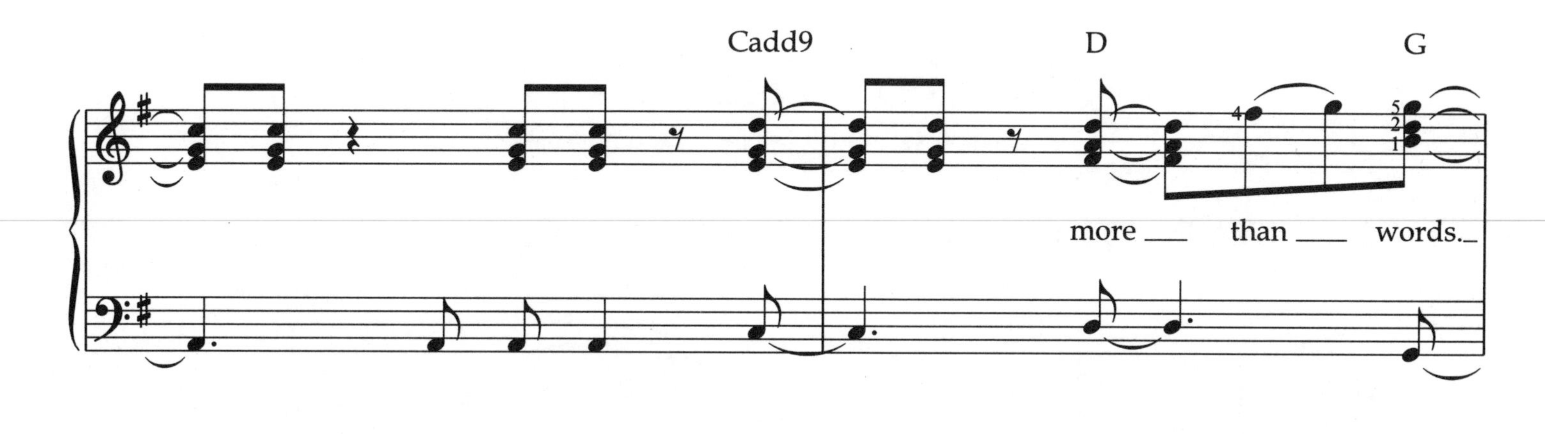

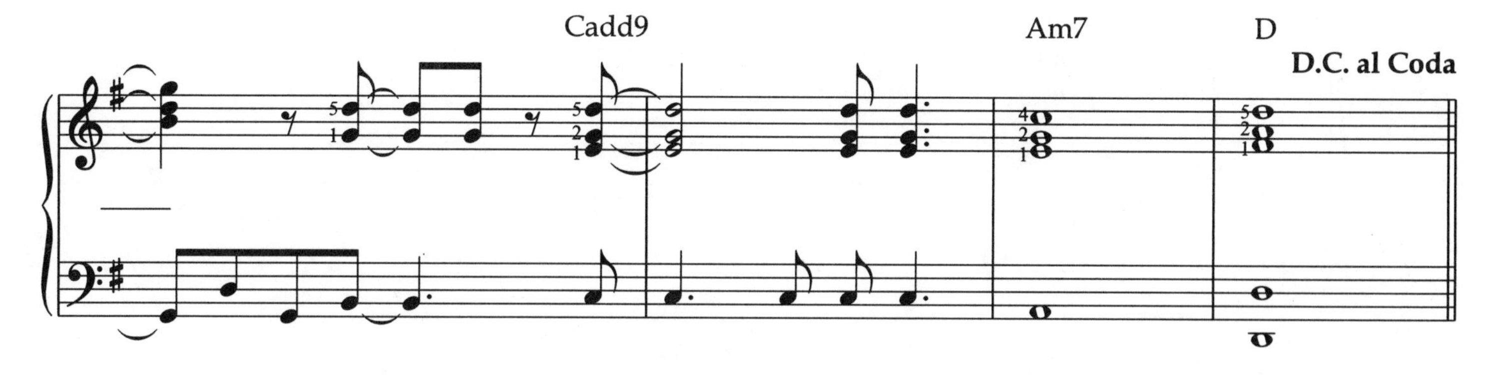

D.C.

Now that I've tried to talk to you
And make you understand
All you have to do is close your eyes
And just reach out your hands
And touch me.
Hold me close, don't ever let me go
More than words
Is all I ever needed you to show
Then you wouldn't have to say
That you love me
'Cause I'd already know.

Tears In Heaven

Words & Music by Eric Clapton & Will Jennings

Am7
C/D
D
G
D/F♯
know I don't be - long here in hea - ven.
know I just can't stay, tears in hea - ven.
know there'll be no more tears in hea - ven.
Em
/D
C/E
Dsus4
D7
G
4th time Fine
rall. last time
B♭
Am7
Gm7
C/E
Time can bring you down, time can bend your knees.
F
C
Dm
C
F
B♭
Am7
Time can break the heart,
D.C. (repeat)
Gm7
C/E
F
C/E
D
Em
D7
have you beg - ging, please, beg- ging please.

To Love Somebody

Words & Music Barry Gibb & Robin Gibb

G
F
G
thing.
you.
But what does it
But what good does it
bring
do
if I ain't got
D
C7
G
you,
ain't got
you.
f
You don't
know
what it's like,
D
C
G
ba - by,
you don't
know
what it's like
to love some
D
C
bod - y,
to love some -
bod - y
the way
I
1.
2.
D.S. and fade
G
G
D
love you.
(mf)
(2.) In my
love you.

Stars

Words & Music by Mick Hucknall

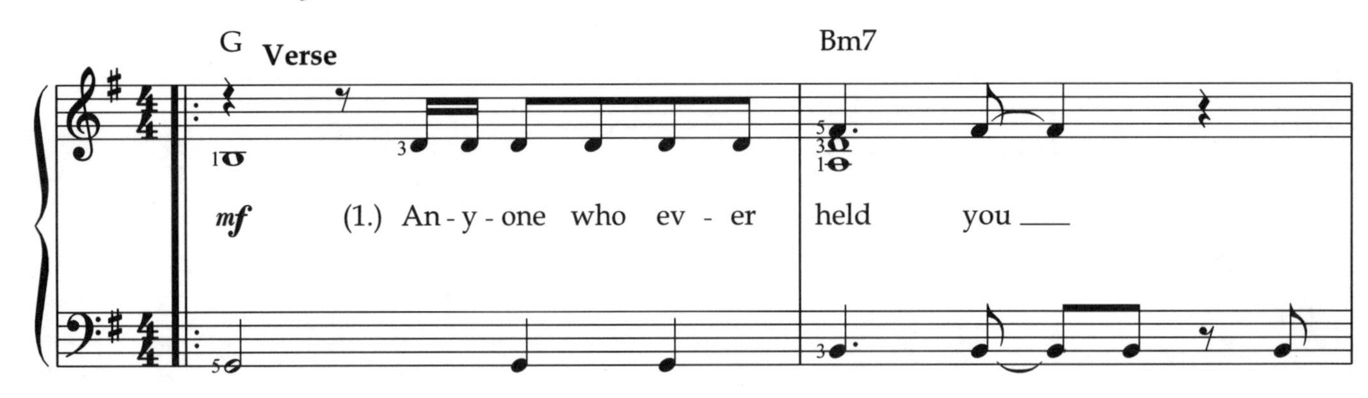

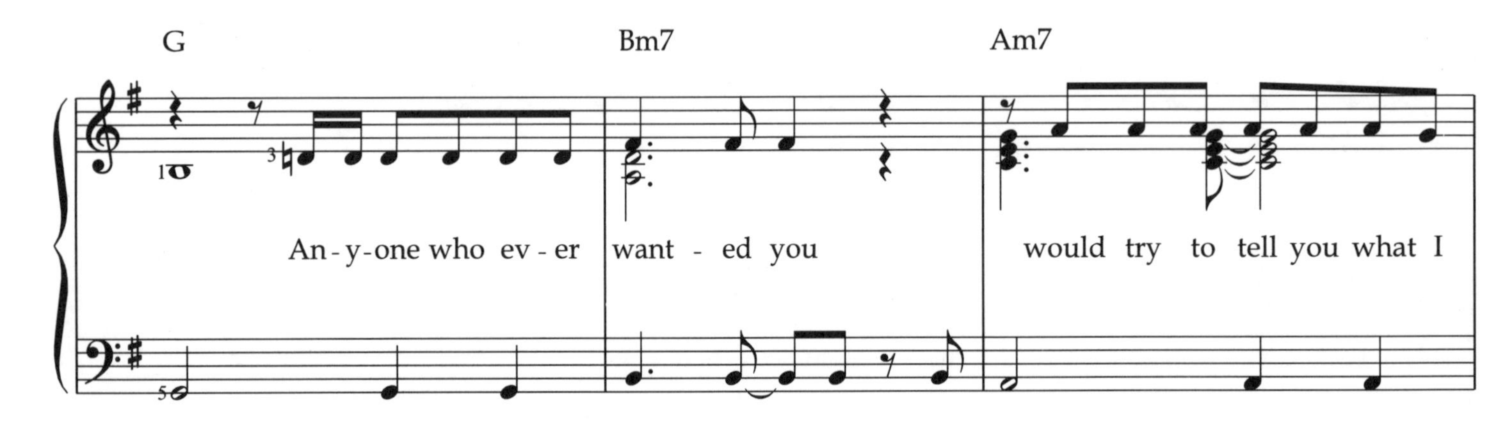

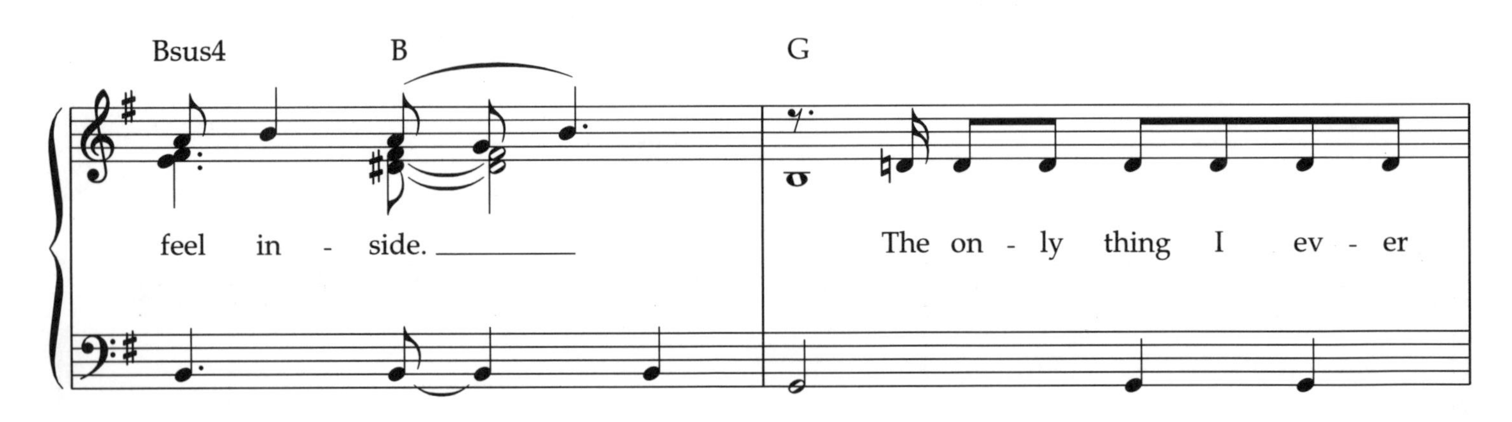

Bm7
Am7
Bsus4
B
want - ed
was the feel-ing that you
ain't fak - ing.
G
Bm7
Am7
The on-ly one who ev-er
thought a-bout,
wait a min-ute, can't
B
G
D/F♯
Chorus
you see
that
I
wan-na fall
from the
Am7
Bsus4
B
G
stars
straight in - to your arms,
I,
D/F♯
Am7
To Coda
(last time)
Bsus4
B
I
feel you,
you,
I
hope you com-pre-hend.

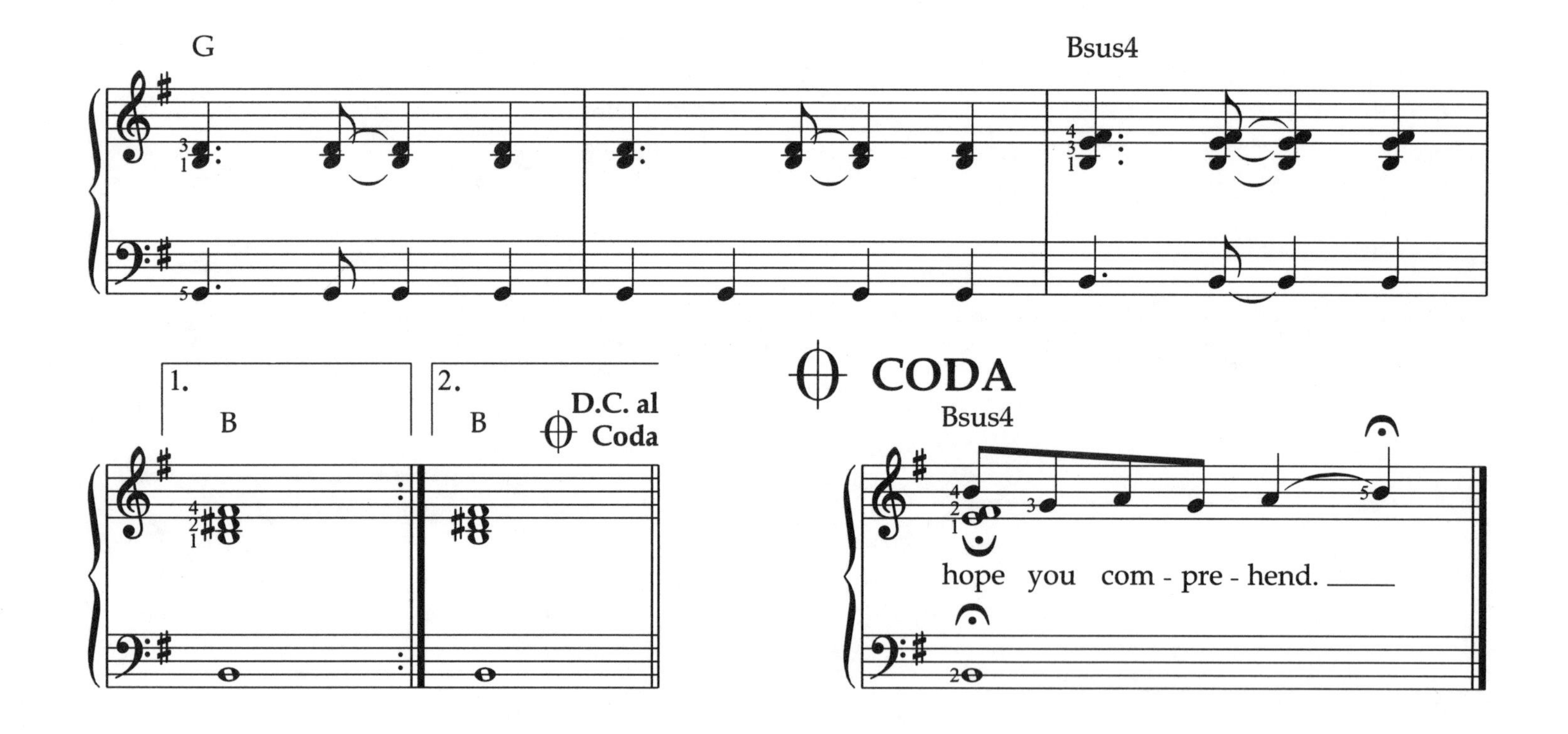

Verse 2

For the man who tried to hurt you,
He's explaining the way I'm feeling.
For all the jealousy I caused you,
States the reason why I'm trying to hide.
As for all the things you taught me,
It sends my future into clearer dimensions.
You'll never know how much you hurt me,
Stay a minute can't you see that:
(To Chorus)

Verse 3

Too many hearts are broken,
A lover's promise never came with a maybe.
So many words are left unspoken,
The silent voices are driving me crazy.
As for all the pain you caused me,
Making up could never be your intention.
You'll never know how much you hurt me,
Stay can't you see that:
(To Chorus)

Intro | C | Am | D | Gsus / G / | 2/4 G ||

When You Tell Me That You Love Me

Words & Music by Albert Hammond & John Bettis

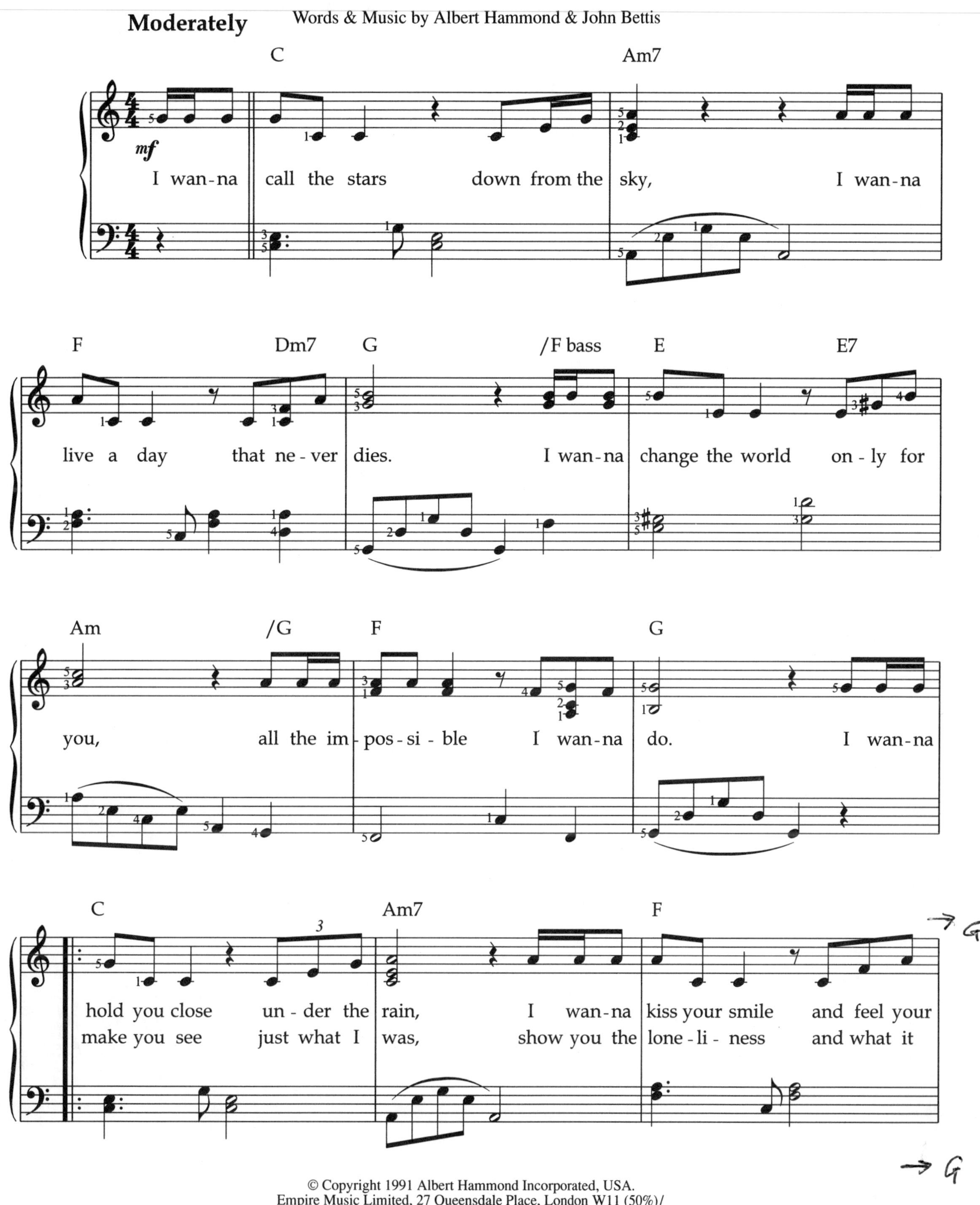

G /F E E7 Am /G
pain, I know what's beau-ti-ful look-ing at you, in a
does, you walked in-to my life to stop my tears, ev'ry-thing's
F G F/G G C
world of lies you are the truth. And ba-by ev'-ry time you touch me,
ea-sy now I have you here.
Am /G F Dm7 G F/G G
I be-come a he-ro, I'll make you safe, no mat-ter where you are. And bring you
C Am F Dm
ev'-ry-thing you ask for, no-thing is a-bove me, I'm shin-ing like a can-dle in the
G To Coda 1. C D/F#
dark when you tell me that you love me.

2.
G
C
A♭
(2.) I wan-na love me.
In a world with-out you,
C
A♭
I will al - ways hun - ger,
all I need is your love to
D.𝄋 al Coda
B♭
A♭/B♭
B♭
E♭
G
F/G
G
make me strong - - er.
And ba - by
cresc.
f
CODA
C
Am7
F
love me.
You
love me,
G
C
Am
C
G7
C
when you tell me that you love me.

Why

Words & Music by Annie Lennox

Fmaj7 G C C/B
trou-ble's on - ly just be - gun.
Am7 Fmaj7 G C
I tell my - self too ma - ny
Am7 C/E Fmaj7 G
times, why don't you e - ver learn to keep your big mouth shut?
C Am7 C/E
That's why it hurts so bad to hear the words that keep on fall - ing from your mouth,
Fmaj7 G E♭maj7
rubato
fall - ing, from your mouth,

C9
D7
C
a tempo
fall - ing from your mouth. Tell me
Why?
C/B
Am7
Fmaj7
G
C
C/B
A7
Fmaj7
G
Why?
C
C/B
This is the book I've ne - ver read,
These are the years that we have spent,
these are the words I ne - ver said,
and this is what they re - pre - sent,
Am7
Fmaj7
G
is this the path I'll ne - ver tread,
and this is how I feel.
these are the dreams I'll dream in - stead,
Do you know how I feel?

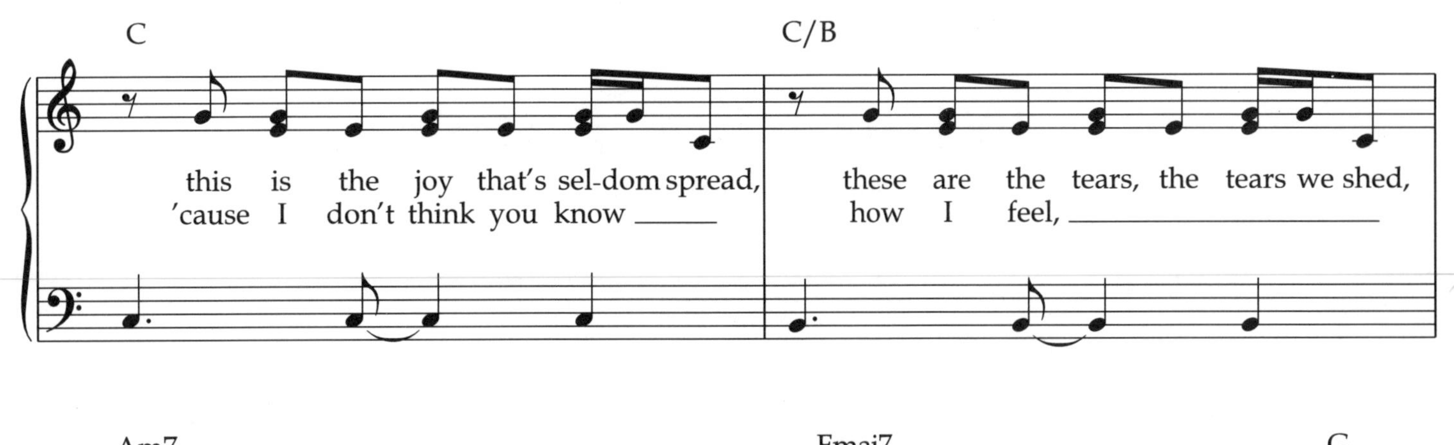

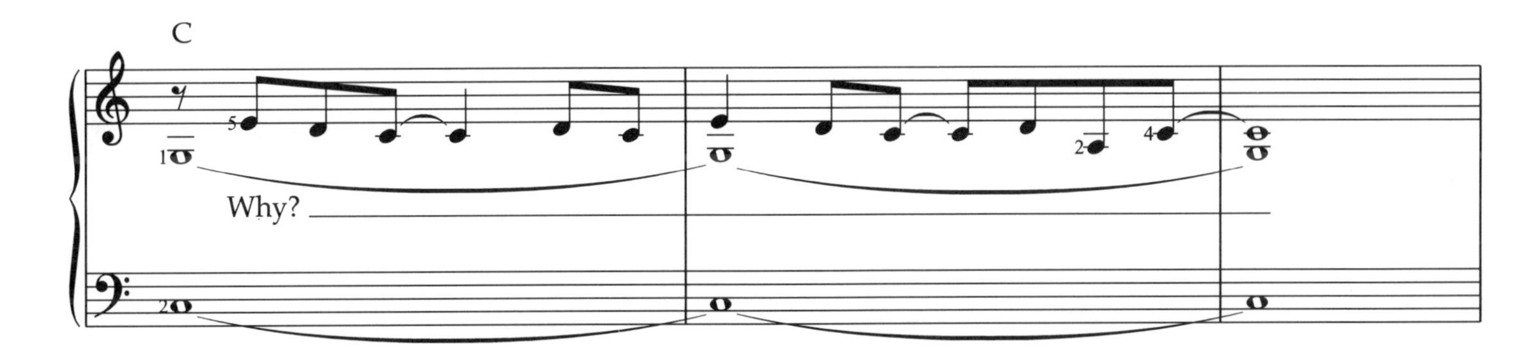

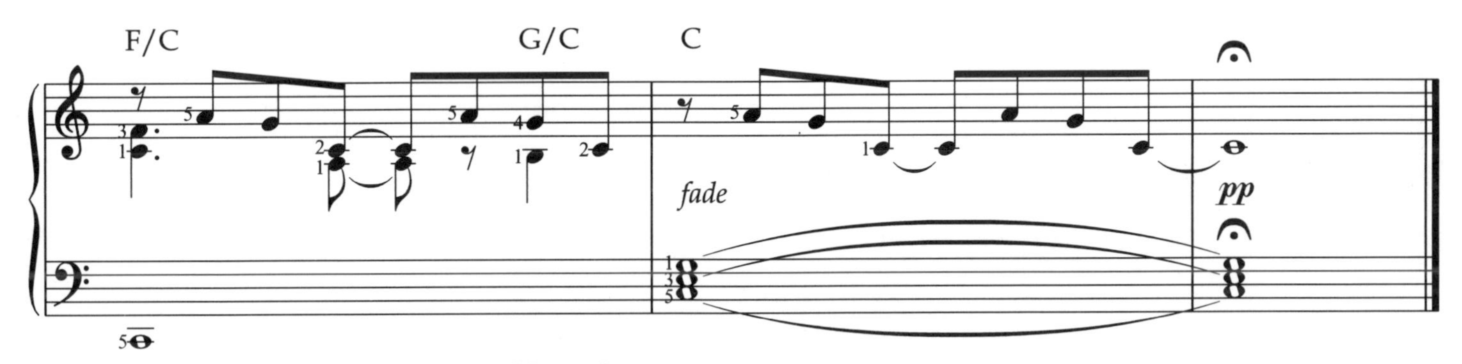

Verse 2

I may be mad, I may be blind,
I may be viciously unkind,
But I can still read what you're thinking.
And I've heard it said too many times
That you'd be better off,
Besides, why can't you see this boat is sinking?

Let's go down to the water's edge
And we can cast away those doubts,
Some things are better left unsaid
But they still turn me inside out.
Turning inside out, turning inside out.

Wind Of Change

Words & Music by Klaus Meine